ROADWORKS

For Alice — why should the boys have all the fun? SS
For Jackie and Harry BL

First published in 2008
by Walker Books Australia Pty Ltd
Locked Bag 22, Newtown
NSW 2042 Australia
www.walkerbooks.com.au

This edition published in 2010.

National Library of Australia Cataloguing-in-Publication entry:

Sutton, Sally.

Roadworks / Sally Sutton; illustrator, Brian Lovelock.

ISBN: 978 1 921529 53 5 (pbk.)

For pre-school age.

Subjects: Roads — Design and construction — Juvenile literature.

          Road machinery — Juvenile literature.

Other Authors/Contributors: Lovelock, Brian, 1956—

625.7

Typeset in Franklin Gothic Extra Condensed

The illustrations for this book were painted with pigmented inks.

Printed and bound in China

10 9 8 7 6 5 4 3 2

Plan the road. Plan the road.

Mark it on the map.

Hammer in the marking pegs.

Ping! BANG! TAP!

Move the earth. Move the earth.

Dig and cut and push.

Clear a pathway for the road.

Screech! BOOM! WHOOSH!

Load the dirt. Load the dirt.
Scoop and swing and drop.
Slam it down into the truck.

Bump!
WHUMP!
WHOP!

Tip the stones. Tip the stones.

Lift and slide and dump.

Lay the groundwork for the road.

Crash! ROAR!

THUMP!

Pack the ground. Pack the ground.

Roll one way, then back.

Make the roadbed good and hard.

Clang! CRUNCH!

CRACK!

Seal the road. Seal the road.

Make it hot and squishy.

Spread the sticky tar and stones.

Sploshy! SPLASHY! SPLISHY!

Roll the tar. Roll the tar.

Make it firm and flat.

Squash it down and press it out.

Squelch! SPLUCK! SPLAT!

Stop the work. Stop the work.

Time to break for lunch.

Sandwiches and drinks and fruit.

Mark the road. Mark the road.

Give the paint a squirt.

Paint the lines in nice and straight.

Whizz! SPLOP!
SPLURT!

Raise the signs. Raise the signs.

Drag and hoist and ram.

Force them down into their holes.

Thwack! WHOP!
WHAM!

Light the road. Light the road.

No one wants a crash.

Test the lights and see them shine.

Flick! FLACK! FLASH!

Plant the trees. Plant the trees.

Dig and stamp and lug.

Water them to help them grow.

Drip! DROP! GLUG!

Tidy up. Tidy up.

Lift and load and sweep.

Drive away those big machines.

Swish! CHUG!

BEEP!

Shout hooray! The work is done.
Ready, now? Let's zoom.
Drive along your brand-new road.